Piano
Scales & Arpeggios
ABRSM Grade 1

from **2021**

Learning scales and arpeggios helps you to build strong technical skills by developing reliable finger movement, hand position, co-ordination and keyboard fluency. It also helps you to develop your musical understanding through familiarity with keys and their related patterns.

You can find a complete list of scales and arpeggios required for Grades Initial–5 in the back of this book. In the exam, scales and arpeggios should be played from memory, legato and without pedalling. The examiner will ask for a selection of the requirements. Further information can be found in the syllabus and at www.abrsm.org.

About this book

The printed pitches have been chosen mainly for ease of reading, and the starting notes may not always be in the most appropriate or comfortable octave(s). You are free to start in a different octave as long as the required range is covered.

You may use any fingerings that produce a successful musical outcome. The fingerings provided are suggestions only, with alternative fingerings shown separated by an oblique sign, for example 4/3. You may explore other fingering options to decide what works best for you.

The metronome marks shown are for guidance only.

These requirements are valid from 1 January 2021 until further notice. Reference must always be made to the syllabus for the year in which the exam is to be taken, in case any changes have been made to the requirements.

Published by ABRSM (Publishing) Ltd, a wholly owned subsidiary of ABRSM
© 2020 by The Associated Board of the Royal Schools of Music
Music origination by Julia Bovee
Printed in England by Page Bros, Norwich, Norfolk, on materials from sustainable sources
P14536

SCALES

hands together (similar motion)

C major

hands separately

two octaves ♩= 60

G major

RH

LH

F major

RH

LH

SCALES (cont.)

hands separately

A minor natural

or

A minor harmonic

or

A minor melodic

D minor natural

RH

LH

or

D minor harmonic

RH

LH

or

D minor melodic

RH

LH

CONTRARY-MOTION SCALE

hands starting on the tonic (unison)

one octave   ♩ = 60

C major

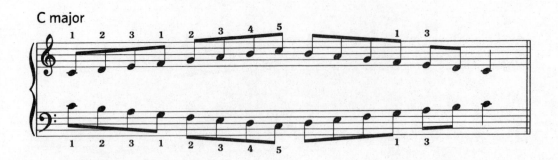

ARPEGGIOS

hands separately

one octave   ♩ = 58

G major

A minor

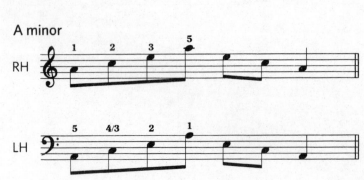

Piano
Scales & Arpeggios
ABRSM Grade 2

from **2021**

Learning scales and arpeggios helps you to build strong technical skills by developing reliable finger movement, hand position, co-ordination and keyboard fluency. It also helps you to develop your musical understanding through familiarity with keys and their related patterns.

You can find a complete list of scales and arpeggios required for Grades Initial–5 in the back of this book. In the exam, scales and arpeggios should be played from memory, legato and without pedalling. The examiner will ask for a selection of the requirements. Further information can be found in the syllabus and at www.abrsm.org.

About this book

The printed pitches have been chosen mainly for ease of reading, and the starting notes may not always be in the most appropriate or comfortable octave(s). You are free to start in a different octave as long as the required range is covered.

You may use any fingerings that produce a successful musical outcome. The fingerings provided are suggestions only, with alternative fingerings shown separated by an oblique sign, for example 4/3. You may explore other fingering options to decide what works best for you.

The metronome marks shown are for guidance only.

These requirements are valid from 1 January 2021 until further notice. Reference must always be made to the syllabus for the year in which the exam is to be taken, in case any changes have been made to the requirements.

Published by ABRSM (Publishing) Ltd, a wholly owned subsidiary of ABRSM
© 2020 by The Associated Board of the Royal Schools of Music

Music origination by Julia Bovee
Printed in England by Page Bros, Norwich, Norfolk, on materials from sustainable sources
P14537

SCALES

hands together (similar motion)

two octaves ♩ = 66

[handwritten: G M scale H.S. :) 8/9/24]

G major

F major

A minor natural

or

A minor harmonic

or

A minor melodic

D minor natural

or

D minor harmonic

or

D minor melodic

hands separately   two octaves   ♩ = 66

D major

RH

LH

A major

RH

LH

SCALES (cont.)

hands separately

E minor natural

E minor harmonic

E minor melodic

G minor natural

RH

LH

or

G minor harmonic

RH

LH

or

G minor melodic

RH

LH

CONTRARY-MOTION SCALE

hands starting on the tonic (unison)

two octaves ♩ = 66

C major

CHROMATIC SCALE

hands separately

one octave ♩ = 66

starting on D

AB 3926

ARPEGGIOS

hands separately

D major

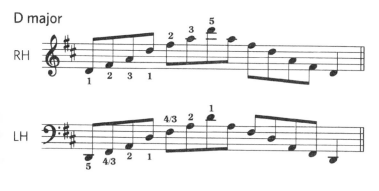

A major

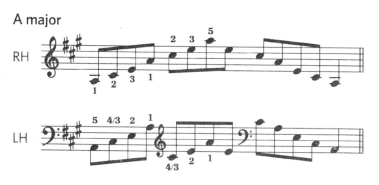

E minor

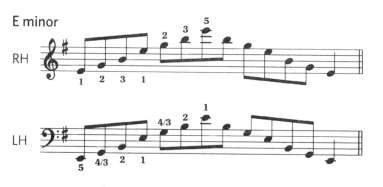

G minor

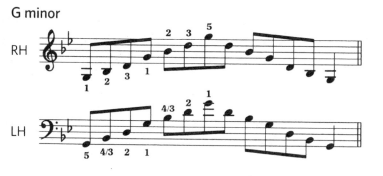

Alternative fingering for right-hand arpeggios: **2 4 1 2 4 1 2**

Piano
Scales & Arpeggios

ABRSM Grade 3

from 2020

Learning scales and arpeggios helps you to build strong technical skills by developing reliable finger movement, hand position, co-ordination and keyboard fluency. It also helps you to develop your musical understanding through familiarity with keys and their related patterns.

You can find a complete list of scales and arpeggios required for Grades Initial–5 in the back of this book. In the exam, scales and arpeggios should be played from memory, legato and without pedalling. The examiner will ask for a selection of the requirements. Further information can be found in the syllabus and at www.abrsm.org.

About this book

The printed pitches have been chosen mainly for ease of reading, and the starting notes may not always be in the most appropriate or comfortable octave(s). You are free to start in a different octave as long as the required range is covered.

You may use any fingerings that produce a successful musical outcome. The fingerings provided are suggestions only, with alternative fingerings shown separated by an oblique sign, for example 4/3. You may explore other fingering options to decide what works best for you.

The metronome marks shown are for guidance only.

These requirements are valid from 1 January 2021 until further notice. Reference must always be made to the syllabus for the year in which the exam is to be taken, in case any changes have been made to the requirements.

Published by ABRSM (Publishing) Ltd, a wholly owned subsidiary of ABRSM
© 2020 by The Associated Board of the Royal Schools of Music

Music origination by Julia Bovee
Printed in England by Page Bros, Norwich, Norfolk, on materials from sustainable sources
P14538

SCALES

hands together (similar motion)

D major

A major

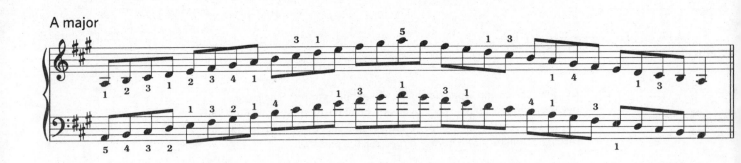

E minor harmonic

or

E minor melodic

AB 3927

G minor harmonic

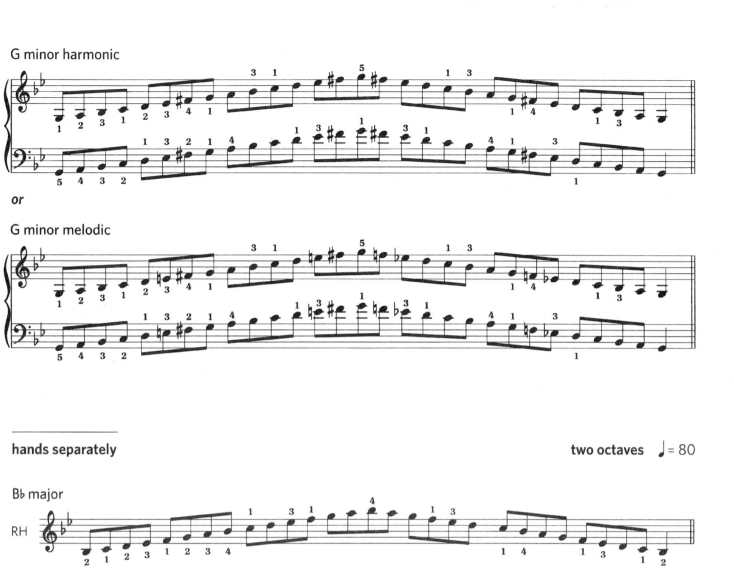

or

G minor melodic

---

hands separately

two octaves ♩ = 80

B♭ major

RH

LH

E♭ major

RH

LH

SCALES (cont.)

hands separately

B minor harmonic

or

B minor melodic

C minor harmonic

or

C minor melodic

CONTRARY-MOTION SCALE

hands starting on the tonic (unison)

two octaves ♩ = 80

E major

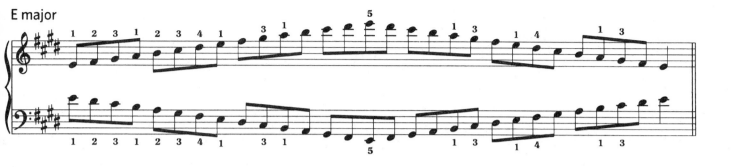

CHROMATIC CONTRARY-MOTION SCALE

hands starting on the stated note (unison)

one octave ♩ = 80

starting on D

ARPEGGIOS

hands together   two octaves ♩ = 72

D major

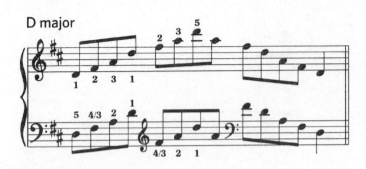

A major

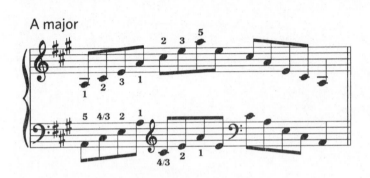

E minor

G minor

hands separately   two octaves ♩ = 72

B♭ major

RH

LH

E♭ major

RH

LH

B minor

RH

LH

C minor

RH

LH

Piano
Scales & Arpeggios
ABRSM Grade 4

from **2021**

Learning scales and arpeggios helps you to build strong technical skills by developing reliable finger movement, hand position, co-ordination and keyboard fluency. It also helps you to develop your musical understanding through familiarity with keys and their related patterns.

You can find a complete list of scales and arpeggios required for Grades Initial–5 in the back of this book. In the exam, scales and arpeggios should be played from memory, legato and without pedalling. The examiner will ask for a selection of the requirements. Further information can be found in the syllabus and at www.abrsm.org.

About this book

The printed pitches have been chosen mainly for ease of reading, and the starting notes may not always be in the most appropriate or comfortable octave(s). You are free to start in a different octave as long as the required range is covered.

You may use any fingerings that produce a successful musical outcome. The fingerings provided are suggestions only, with alternative fingerings shown separated by an oblique sign, for example 4/3. You may explore other fingering options to decide what works best for you.

The metronome marks shown are for guidance only.

These requirements are valid from 1 January 2021 until further notice. Reference must always be made to the syllabus for the year in which the exam is to be taken, in case any changes have been made to the requirements.

Published by ABRSM (Publishing) Ltd, a wholly owned subsidiary of ABRSM
© 2020 by The Associated Board of the Royal Schools of Music
Music origination by Julia Bovee
Printed in England by Page Bros, Norwich, Norfolk, on materials from sustainable sources
P14539

SCALES

hands together (similar motion)

AB 3928

C minor harmonic

or

C minor melodic

___

hands separately

two octaves ♩ = 100

B major

RH

LH

F# major

RH

LH

A♭ major

RH

LH

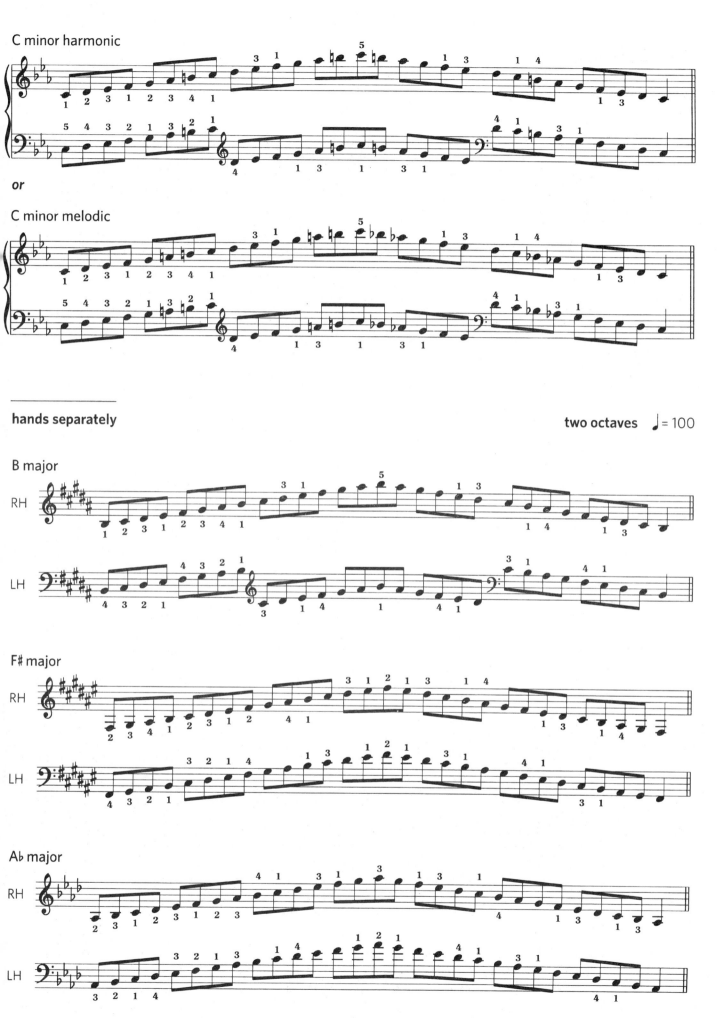

AB 3928

3

SCALES (cont.)

hands separately

F# minor harmonic

F# minor melodic

F minor harmonic

or

F minor melodic

CONTRARY-MOTION SCALES

hands starting on the tonic (unison)

Eb major

C minor harmonic

CHROMATIC SCALE

hands together (similar motion)

two octaves   ♩ = 100

starting on F#

One octave only is printed here, as finger patterns are sufficiently established within this range.

ARPEGGIOS

hands together

Bb major

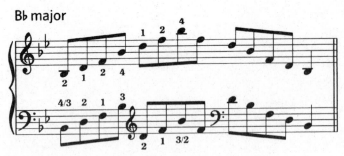

Eb major

B minor

C minor

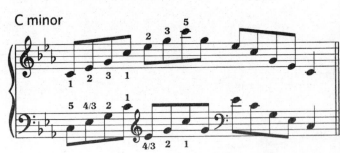

hands separately

B major

RH 

LH 

F# major

RH 

LH 

Ab major

RH

LH

F# minor

RH

LH

F minor

RH

LH

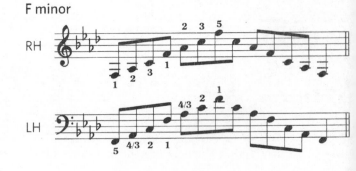

AB 3928

Piano
Scales & Arpeggios
ABRSM Grade 5

from **2021**

Learning scales and arpeggios helps you to build strong technical skills by developing reliable finger movement, hand position, co-ordination and keyboard fluency. It also helps you to develop your musical understanding through familiarity with keys and their related patterns.

You can find a complete list of scales and arpeggios required for Grades Initial–5 in the back of this book. In the exam, scales and arpeggios should be played from memory and without pedalling. The examiner will ask for a selection of the requirements. Further information can be found in the syllabus and at www.abrsm.org.

About this book

The printed pitches have been chosen mainly for ease of reading, and the starting notes may not always be in the most appropriate or comfortable octave(s). You are free to start in a different octave as long as the required range is covered.

You may use any fingerings that produce a successful musical outcome. The fingerings provided are suggestions only, with alternative fingerings shown separated by an oblique sign, for example 4/3. You may explore other fingering options to decide what works best for you.

The metronome marks shown are for guidance only.

These requirements are valid from 1 January 2021 until further notice. Reference must always be made to the syllabus for the year in which the exam is to be taken, in case any changes have been made to the requirements.

Published by ABRSM (Publishing) Ltd, a wholly owned subsidiary of ABRSM
© 2020 by The Associated Board of the Royal Schools of Music

Music origination by Julia Bovee
Printed in England by Page Bros, Norwich, Norfolk, on materials from sustainable sources
P14540

SCALES

hands together (similar motion)
legato

A major

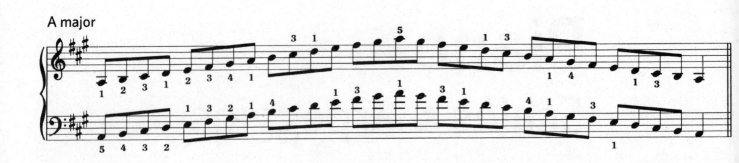

E major

B major

F# major

D♭ major

F# minor harmonic

or

F# minor melodic

C# minor harmonic

or

C# minor melodic

G# minor harmonic

or

G# minor melodic

SCALES (cont.)

hands together (similar motion)
legato

righttwo octaves ♩ = 60

Eb minor harmonic

or

Eb minor melodic

Bb minor harmonic

or

Bb minor melodic

AB 3929

STACCATO SCALES

hands separately

A♭ major

F minor harmonic

or

F minor melodic

CONTRARY-MOTION SCALES

hands starting on the tonic (unison)
legato

two octaves ♩ = 60

Db major

C# minor harmonic

CHROMATIC CONTRARY-MOTION SCALE

hands starting a major third apart
legato

two octaves ♩ = 60

starting on F# (LH) and A# (RH)

One octave only is printed here, as finger patterns are sufficiently established within this range.

ARPEGGIOS

hands together
legato

A major

F# minor

E major

C# minor

B major

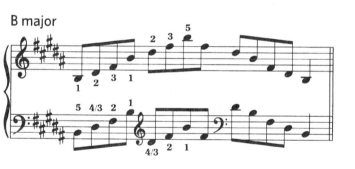

G# minor

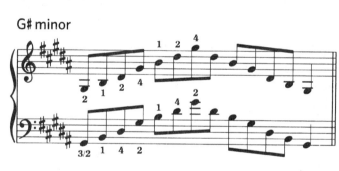

F# major

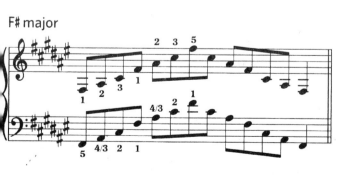

E♭ minor

ARPEGGIOS (cont.)

hands together
legato

A♭ major

F minor

D♭ major

B♭ minor

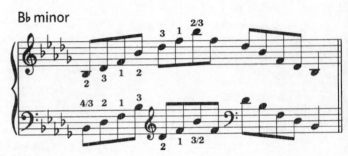

DIMINISHED SEVENTH

hands separately
legato

two octaves   ♩ = 44

starting on B

AB 3929

Piano
Scales & Arpeggios
ABRSM Grade 6

from 2021

Learning scales and arpeggios helps you to build strong technical skills by developing reliable finger movement, hand position, co-ordination and keyboard fluency. It also helps you to develop your musical understanding through familiarity with keys and their related patterns.

You can find a complete list of scales and arpeggios required for Grades 6–8 in the back of this book. In the exam, scales and arpeggios should be played from memory and without pedalling. The examiner will ask for a selection of the requirements. Further information can be found in the syllabus and at www.abrsm.org.

About this book

The requirements are printed in this book up to a two-octave range, as this is sufficient to establish finger patterns.

The printed pitches have been chosen mainly for ease of reading, and the starting notes may not always be in the most appropriate or comfortable octave(s). You are free to start in a different octave as long as the required range is covered.

You may use any fingerings that produce a successful musical outcome. The fingerings provided are suggestions only, with alternative fingerings shown separated by an oblique sign, for example 4/3. You may explore other fingering options to decide what works best for you.

The metronome marks shown are for guidance only.

These requirements are valid from 1 January 2021 until further notice. Reference must always be made to the syllabus for the year in which the exam is to be taken, in case any changes have been made to the requirements.

Published by ABRSM (Publishing) Ltd, a wholly owned subsidiary of ABRSM
© 2020 by The Associated Board of the Royal Schools of Music
Music origination by Julia Bovee
Printed in England by Page Bros, Norwich, Norfolk, on materials from sustainable sources
P14541

SCALES

hands together (similar motion)
legato *or* staccato, at examiner's choice

four octaves ♩ = 72

D major

F major

A♭ major

B major

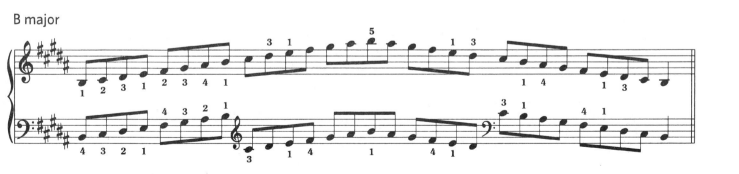

SCALES (cont.)

hands together (similar motion)
legato *or* staccato, at examiner's choice

four octaves   ♩ = 72

D minor harmonic

D minor melodic

F minor harmonic

F minor melodic

AB 3930

G# minor harmonic

G# minor melodic

B minor harmonic

B minor melodic

CONTRARY-MOTION SCALES

hands starting on the tonic (unison)
legato

D major

F major

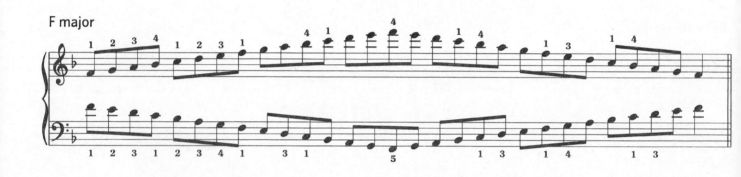

A♭ major

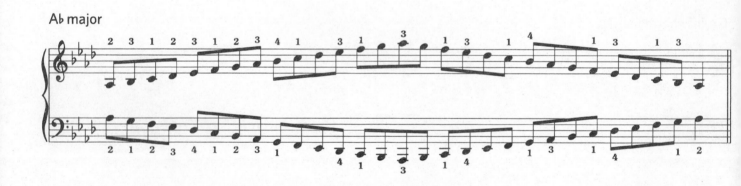

B major

D minor harmonic

F minor harmonic

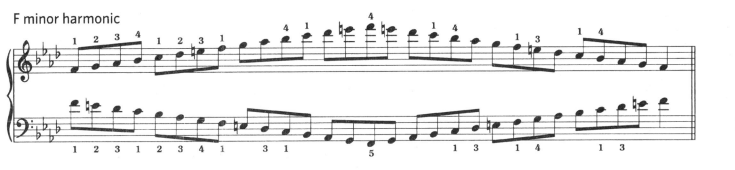

G# minor harmonic

B minor harmonic

CHROMATIC SCALES

hands together (similar motion)
legato *or* **staccato, at examiner's choice**

four octaves ♩ = 72

starting on G#

starting on B

AB 3930

ARPEGGIOS

hands together (root position)
legato

D major

D minor

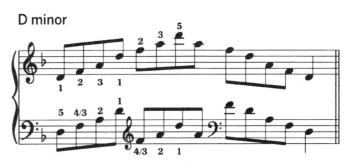

F major

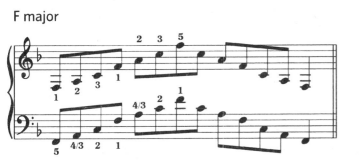

F minor

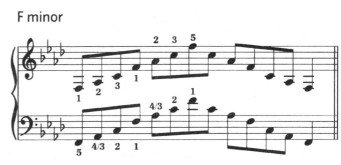

A♭ major

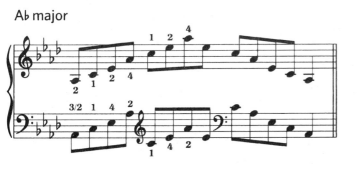

G♯ minor

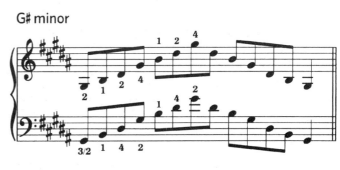

B major

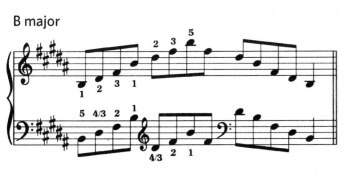

B minor

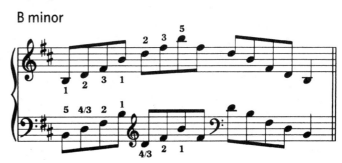

DOMINANT SEVENTHS

hands together
legato
resolving on the tonic

in the key of D

in the key of F

in the key of A♭

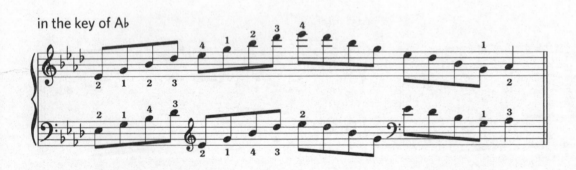

in the key of B

DIMINISHED SEVENTHS

hands together
legato

starting on G#

starting on B

Piano
Scales & Arpeggios

ABRSM Grade 7

from 2021

Learning scales and arpeggios helps you to build strong technical skills by developing reliable finger movement, hand position, co-ordination and keyboard fluency. It also helps you to develop your musical understanding through familiarity with keys and their related patterns.

You can find a complete list of scales and arpeggios required for Grades 6–8 in the back of this book. In the exam, scales and arpeggios should be played from memory and without pedalling. The examiner will ask for a selection of the requirements. Further information can be found in the syllabus and at www.abrsm.org.

About this book

The requirements are printed in this book up to a two-octave range, as this is sufficient to establish finger patterns.

The printed pitches have been chosen mainly for ease of reading, and the starting notes may not always be in the most appropriate or comfortable octave(s). You are free to start in a different octave as long as the required range is covered.

You may use any fingerings that produce a successful musical outcome. The fingerings provided are suggestions only, with alternative fingerings shown separated by an oblique sign, for example 4/3. You may explore other fingering options to decide what works best for you.

The metronome marks shown are for guidance only.

These requirements are valid from 1 January 2021 until further notice. Reference must always be made to the syllabus for the year in which the exam is to be taken, in case any changes have been made to the requirements.

Published by ABRSM (Publishing) Ltd, a wholly owned subsidiary of ABRSM
© 2020 by The Associated Board of the Royal Schools of Music

Music origination by Julia Bovee
Printed in England by Page Bros, Norwich, Norfolk, on materials from sustainable sources
P14542

SCALES

hands together (similar motion)
legato *or* staccato, at examiner's choice

four octaves ♩= 80

2

AB 3931

E minor harmonic

E minor melodic

G minor harmonic

G minor melodic

B♭ minor harmonic

B♭ minor melodic

SCALES A THIRD APART

hands together
legato *or* **staccato, at examiner's choice**

four octaves   ♩= 60

Db major

E major

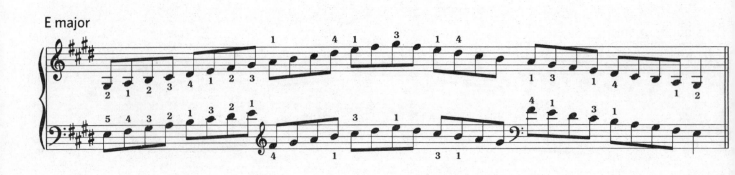

G major

Bb major

C# minor harmonic

E minor harmonic

G minor harmonic

Bb minor harmonic

CONTRARY-MOTION SCALES

hands starting on the tonic (unison)
legato *or* staccato, at examiner's choice

two octaves   ♩ = 80

Db major

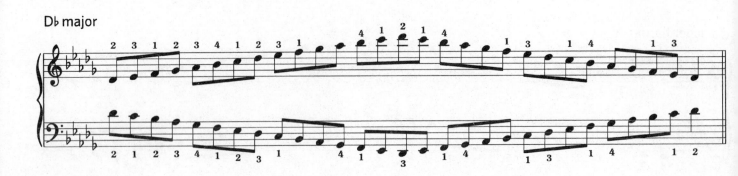

E major

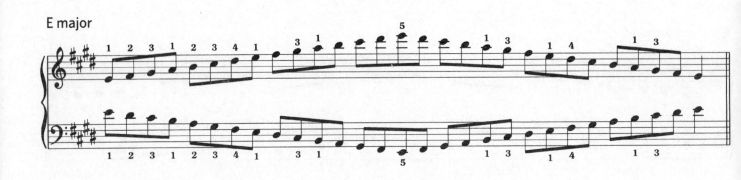

G major

Bb major

AB 3931

C# minor harmonic

E minor harmonic

G minor harmonic

Bb minor harmonic

LEGATO SCALE IN THIRDS and STACCATO SCALE IN THIRDS

hands separately

two octaves
legato: ♩ = 46
staccato: ♩ = 54

G major

alternative fingering

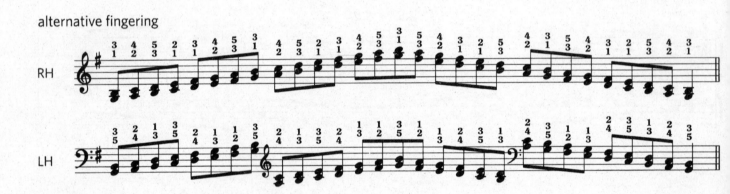

CHROMATIC CONTRARY-MOTION SCALE

hands starting a minor third apart
legato *or* staccato, at examiner's choice

two octaves   ♩ = 80

starting on C♯ (LH) and E (RH)

ARPEGGIOS

hands together
legato
first inversion only

Db major

C# minor

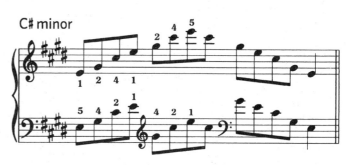

E major

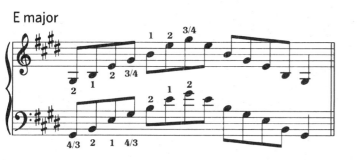

E minor

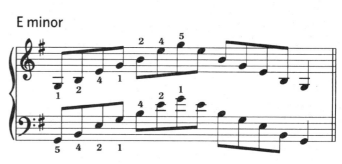

G major

G minor

Bb major

Bb minor

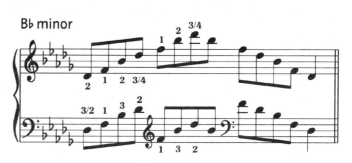

DOMINANT SEVENTHS

hands together
legato
resolving on the tonic

in the key of D♭

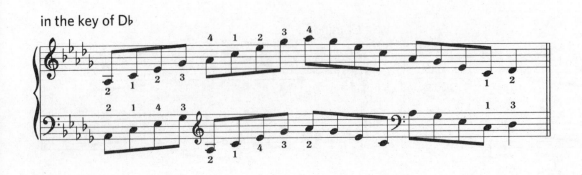

in the key of E

in the key of G

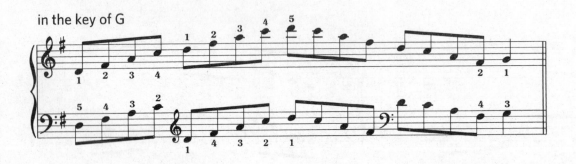

in the key of B♭

DIMINISHED SEVENTHS

hands together
legato

starting on B♭

starting on E

For practical purposes, the diminished seventh starting on B♭ is notated using some enharmonic equivalents.

Piano
Scales & Arpeggios
ABRSM Grade 8

from **2021**

Learning scales and arpeggios helps you to build strong technical skills by developing reliable finger movement, hand position, co-ordination and keyboard fluency. It also helps you to develop your musical understanding through familiarity with keys and their related patterns.

You can find a complete list of scales and arpeggios required for Grades 6–8 in the back of this book. In the exam, scales and arpeggios should be played from memory and without pedalling. The examiner will ask for a selection of the requirements. Further information can be found in the syllabus and at www.abrsm.org.

About this book

The requirements are printed in this book up to a two-octave range, as this is sufficient to establish finger patterns.

The printed pitches have been chosen mainly for ease of reading, and the starting notes may not always be in the most appropriate or comfortable octave(s). You are free to start in a different octave as long as the required range is covered.

You may use any fingerings that produce a successful musical outcome. The fingerings provided are suggestions only, with alternative fingerings shown separated by an oblique sign, for example 3/4. You may explore other fingering options to decide what works best for you.

The metronome marks shown are for guidance only.

These requirements are valid from 1 January 2021 until further notice. Reference must always be made to the syllabus for the year in which the exam is to be taken, in case any changes have been made to the requirements.

Published by ABRSM (Publishing) Ltd, a wholly owned subsidiary of ABRSM
© 2020 by The Associated Board of the Royal Schools of Music
Music origination by Julia Bovee
Printed in England by Page Bros, Norwich, Norfolk, on materials from sustainable sources
P14543

SCALES

hands together (similar motion)
legato *or* staccato, at examiner's choice

four octaves   ♩= 88

AB 3932

Eb minor harmonic

Eb minor melodic

F# minor harmonic

F# minor melodic

A minor harmonic

A minor melodic

SCALES A SIXTH APART

hands together
legato *or* staccato, at examiner's choice

C major

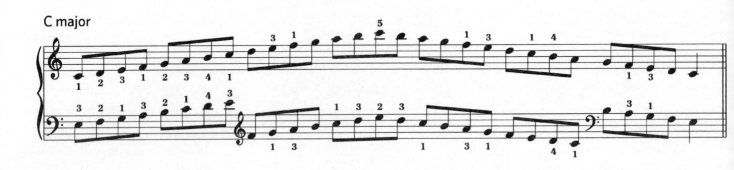

E♭ major

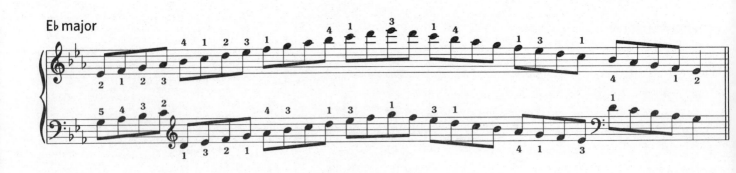

F♯ major

A major

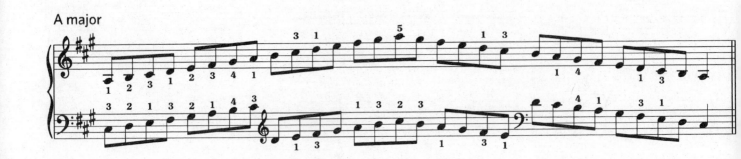

C minor harmonic

E♭ minor harmonic

F♯ minor harmonic

A minor harmonic

CONTRARY-MOTION SCALES

hands starting on the tonic (unison)
legato *or* **staccato, at examiner's choice**

C major

E♭ major

F♯ major

A major

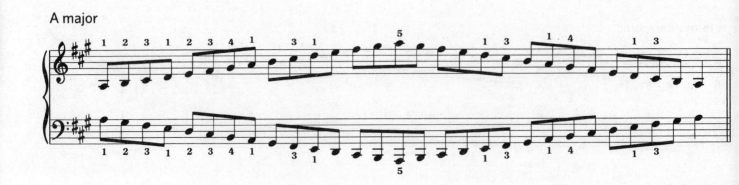

C minor harmonic

E♭ minor harmonic

F♯ minor harmonic

A minor harmonic

LEGATO SCALE IN THIRDS

hands separately

two octaves   ♩ = 52

Eb major

RH

LH

alternative fingering

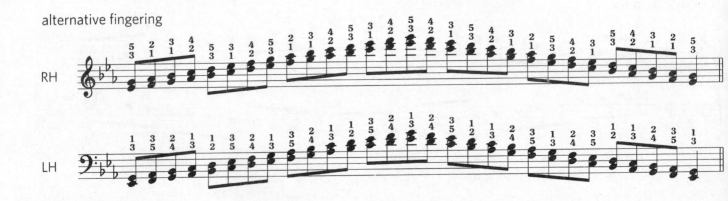

RH

LH

STACCATO SCALE IN SIXTHS

hands separately

two octaves   ♩ = 54

C major

RH

LH

AB 3932

CHROMATIC SCALE A MAJOR SIXTH APART

hands together
legato *or* **staccato, at examiner's choice**

four octaves ♩ = 60

starting on E♭ (LH) and C (RH)

WHOLE-TONE SCALES

hands together (similar motion)
legato *or* **staccato, at examiner's choice**

four octaves ♩ = 88

starting on E♭

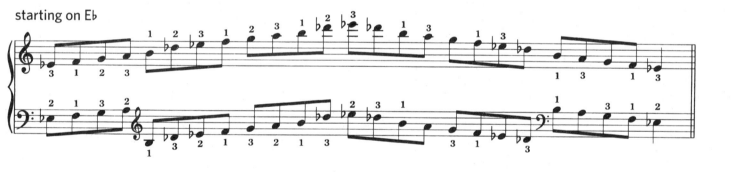

starting on C

ARPEGGIOS

hands together
legato
second inversion only

C major

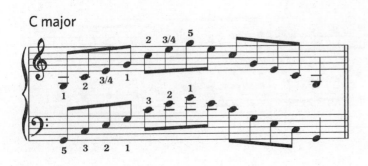

C minor

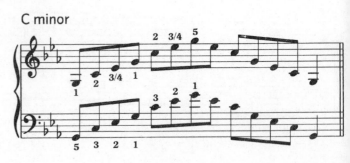

Eb major

Eb minor

F# major

F# minor

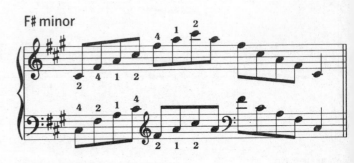

A major

A minor

AB 3932

DOMINANT SEVENTHS

hands together
legato
resolving on the tonic

in the key of C

in the key of E♭

in the key of F♯

in the key of A

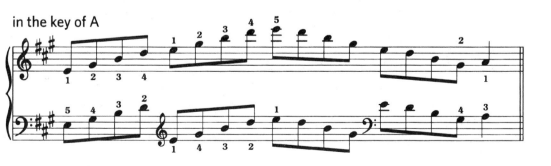

DIMINISHED SEVENTHS

hands together
legato

starting on E♭

starting on C

For practical purposes, the diminished sevenths are notated using some enharmonic equivalents.

        AB 3932